The Encyclopedia
of
Immaturity®

SHORT ATTENTION SPAN EDITION

by the editors of Klutz

KLUTZ®

KLUTZ

creates activity books and other great stuff for kids ages 3 to 103. We began our corporate life in 1977 in a garage we shared with a Chevrolet Impala. Although we've outgrown that first office, Klutz galactic headquarters remains in Palo Alto, California, and we're still staffed entirely by real human beings. For those of you who collect mission statements, here's ours:
• Create wonderful things • Be good • Have fun

Write Us
We would love to hear your comments regarding this or any of our books. We have many!

KLUTZ

450 Lambert Avenue
Palo Alto, CA 94306
thefolks@klutz.com

Manufactured in Korea. 91

Distributed in the UK by
Scholastic UK Ltd
Westfield Road
Southam, Warwickshire
England CV47 0RA

Distributed in Canada by
Scholastic Canada Ltd
604 King Street West
Toronto, Ontario
Canada M5V 1E1

Distributed in Australia by
Scholastic Australia Ltd
PO Box 579
Gosford, NSW
Australia 2250

Distributed in Hong Kong by
Scholastic Hong Kong Ltd
Suites 2001-2, Top Glory Tower
262 Gloucester Road
Causeway Bay, Hong Kong

ISBN 978-0-545-61115-2

4 1 5 8 5 7 0 8 8 8

Introduction

What are you going to be when you grow up?

That's one of those nasty questions people (like teachers and parents) insist on asking. But the question contains an assumption: You have to grow up.

That's an assumption that we here at Klutz would like to challenge. Getting older is inevitable. But growing up is not. With sufficient dedication, you too can remain contentedly and unquestionably immature.

To assist in this worthy effort, we published the first volume of our *Encyclopedia of Immaturity*® back in 2007 — 400 pages of antics, activities, and ideas that would help any dedicated individual postpone that whole growing up thing. We found, to our delight, that many were eager to embrace the joys of immaturity. Fortunately, we had more knowledge to share. Our second volume offered another 200 pages of immature inspiration.

The book you are holding is a highly condensed immaturity sampler, with skills, antics, activities, and ideas from Volumes 1 and 2. Think of it as the CliffsNotes® version.

We hope you'll find that this is one case where reading the CliffsNotes® will inspire you to read the original. Fortunately for you, there's plenty more immaturity where this came from.

— the editors of Klutz

Table of Contents

The Klutz
maturity quiz

How Old Are You Really?

You actually have two ages: One, your "birthday age," which you can get by counting the years since you were born, and two, your real age, which you can get by taking this maturity test and then adding (or subtracting) a maturity factor from your birthday age.

❑ Y Have you ever replaced the toilet paper
❑ N without being told?

❑ Y Do you think cereal that makes your milk
❑ N turn chocolate is a bad thing?

❑ Y Do you think it's unsafe
❑ N to walk up the slide?

❑ Y Can you give someone an "underdog"
❑ N in class if they're sitting in front of you?

❑ Y Can you get a noogie in
❑ N a sandwich?

❑ Y How about a wedgie?
❑ N

❑ Y When you roast
❑ N marshmallows, are you OK
      with either brown or black?

❑ Y Do you know what "IRS"
❑ N stands for?

SCORING

Each "yes" or "don't know" is worth +1 year.

Each "no" is worth −1 year.

How to Read Grown-Up Minds

Ask the nearest grown-up the following questions. Tell them it's part of an important nationwide survey and thank them for participating.

1. "Think of some country that starts with D. Don't tell me what it is." (Typical grown-up will think: *Denmark*.)

2. "Take the last letter of that country and think of any animal that starts with it. Again, don't tell me what it is." (Typical grown-up will think: *kangaroo*.)

3. "Take the last letter of that animal and think of a fruit that starts with it. Don't say anything, just think." (Typical grown-up will think: *orange*.)

4 Finally, put your hand on their forehead, close your eyes, and say the following:

"Orange... you're thinking of an orange."

Typical grown-up

The nastiest activity in this book

How to Fake a Sneeze!

1 Wet your hand under a faucet.

2 Stand behind someone (maybe you're in line?) and fake the sound of a huge, sloppy sneeze. Simultaneously, shake the water on your hand onto the back of their neck.

3 When they turn around, say "Bless me!" and sniffle a few times. Smile.

How to Make Noises Under Your Arm

earning how to make rude noises under your arm can lead to a better life, a better job, higher pay and more friends. Or at least different friends. To learn the basics, just follow the photographic instructions, but be aware that there is greatness out there for those who choose to pursue it. A guy in Texas can do the University of Texas fight song under his arm. If you go onto the internet (we were too frightened) you might be able to find achievements even more dazzling.

1 Identify which hand you're going to use.

2 Cup it.

3 Insert…

4 …under arm.

5 Lift and…

6 …squeeze.

7 Lift and…

8 …squeeze. Repeat.

How Do You Say "Poop" in Potsdam?

People in Potsdam speak German, so "poop" translates to "kot." If you cross the border into France, say "caca," which, by the way, is the most common word for poop around the world. Use it whenever you're abroad and in doubt.

But for those times you're not in a "caca" country, here's a handy tip sheet for travelers.

HERE'S HOW TO SAY POOP IN:

Icelandic: kúkur
German: kot
Hindi: tatti
Bengali: hagu
Japanese: unchi
Tagalog (Philippines): dumi
Slovene: kakec
Mandarin: da bien
Australian/N.Z.: poo
Korean: gomul
Arabic (Palestinian): khara
Swahili: kinyesi
Afrikaans: agsterstewe

How to Kick a Toilet Plunger Field Goal

Set a toilet plunger on the floor about two feet (60 cm) in front of the fridge. Your mother might like it to be clean. We don't care.

In either case, wind up and kick the plunger on the rubber part. Your goal is to stick the thing to the door. This won't happen the first time. If it did, it wouldn't be so special. But after just a few minutes of practice...

2 ft. (60 cm)

The Universal Book Report

Sometimes, in our busy lives, we get stuck having to write a book report about a book whose details we don't entirely remember. That used to be a problem. Now, all you have to do is copy *The Universal Book Report* and fill in the blanks where it says! Life just got simpler!

After reading _____ by
_____ I am full of thoughts.
Never before have I thought the
thoughts that I am now thinking. And
the feelings I am feeling are surely a
result of those thoughts.

The lead character in _____
was, I truly believe, the most important
person. At the beginning of the book, we
don't know him/her very well. Later on,
of course, many difficult things happen
and he/she changes. Near the end of the
book, toward the back, the problems
are fixed and things work out, more or
less. I was so relieved! In conclusion,
I think we all learned an important
lesson! I know that I certainly did!

Thank you.

The End.

How to Predict Your Height

The following formula has been used by real scientists.

Measure your mother and father.

If you're a girl, subtract 5 inches from your father's height. If you're a boy, add 5 inches to your mother's height. Add the adjusted heights of your parents and divide by 2.

To that number, add 2 inches to determine the upper limit of your predicted height. Subtract 2 inches to determine the lower limit of your predicted height. Your final height has a 90% chance of falling within those two limits.

Note: If you're working in metric, remember that 1 inch = 2.5 cm.

Backseat Rituals

Sitting in the backseat of a car does not come without responsibilities. Please read and observe the following rituals. They're ancient and they matter. Don't ask why.

Graveyards and Tunnels

Whenever you drive by a graveyard, you must hold your breath until you have passed it entirely. This rule also holds for all tunnels.

Punchbuggy

Whoever sees a Volkswagen® Beetle and hollers "Punchbuggy" first, gets to punch his seatmate in the shoulder.

Hay Wagon Wishes

If you see a truck filled with hay, make a wish, and if you don't see the truck again, your wish will come true.

Padiddle

If you are the first to see a car with only one headlight working, you holler **"Padiddle!"** and kiss the person next to you. If you are squeamish, you can touch the roof instead.

Trucker Honk

If you see a big truck, the 18-wheeler kind, look hopefully at the driver and pump your arm up and down, as if you were pulling a steam whistle on an old train. The friendlier drivers will honk for you.

River Crossings

Whenever you cross a bridge, you must lift your feet (so they don't get wet).

Cow Alert

If you are the first to spot a cow, you get to holler "Cow Alert!" and everyone else holds their noses and says "Peeee Euuuuuw!"

Give Your Dog a Yawn

1 Stand in front of your dog and open your mouth really wide.

2 Leave it there for a while and make little groaning noises.

3 Repeat as necessary until your dog catches it.

EXTRA CREDIT:

We have given yawns to cats and dogs many times. But to our knowledge, no one in recorded history has ever given a yawn to any other species. Many leading yawn scientists believe it is impossible. We strongly disagree, and we are asking the public for help. If you can give a yawn to any of the following species, please send us a photo, or at least swear to it in an e-mail. Science needs your help!

Yes! I was able to give a yawn to a:
☐ horse
☐ rabbit
☐ cow
☐ bug
☐ fish
☐ hamster
☐ lizard
☐ frog

How to Shake Ankles

1 Approach as if for normal handshake.

2 Reach for hand... but miss to the outside.

3 Lean over, grab their ankle and shake vigorously. So that they may do the same, lift your own ankle up simultaneously.

A quick reference

Homework
Excuses

Sometimes, you just don't really know why you didn't do your homework last night. If that's your problem, check the next page for possible answers.

I sprained my brain. The doctor says no heavy thinking for a week.

I have a rare paper allergy.

Why should I do homework when the universe is winding down and the sun will explode in 5 billion years?

I already finished school in a previous lifetime. I'm only going now for the lunches.

Excuse me? I don't speak English. But thank you for asking. One day I hope to learn your language. In the meantime, I'm just faking it.

I finished my homework in my head. Why write it down and waste a tree?

My horoscope said, "Avoid homework or you will turn into a frog." Can you believe it, Mom? A frog! Whew! We dodged a bullet.

Didn't you hear about the kid who got TOO smart? He made his mom and dad feel dumb. I would never do that to my parents.

I have decided to submit last night's homework to a major broadcaster for a television sitcom pilot. In the meantime, my agent tells me that I can't show it to anyone else.

Department of Dodged Bullets

What's Your "Almost Name"?

What do you think life would have been like if you had been named something like Casper? Or Erma? Pretty scary, huh?

Well, guess what! Real-life parents actually consider these kinds of names when they are getting ready to name their babies! It's true!

HELLO
My Almost Name Is

Ask your own parents what your "almost name" was. You won't believe how close you came to a life of shame and embarrassment.

P.S. A former governor of Texas, James Hogg, actually did name his little girl Ima.

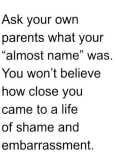

Dumb Jokes

To be truly immature, you need to have an awful joke for every occasion. Here's a starter set of our favorites.

Why do golfers wear two pairs of pants? In case they get a hole in one.

Who yelled, "Coming are the British."? Paul Reverse.

Do you know why gorillas have such big nostrils? Have you ever seen their fingers?

What do you get when you pour boiling water down a rabbit hole? Hot cross bunnies.

If at first you don't succeed, do not try skydiving.

How do you make an elephant fly? First, you start with a 48-inch zipper...

Duck walks into a drugstore and asks, "Do you sell lip balm?"

Clerk says, "Yeah. But how are you going to pay for it?"

Duck says, "Oh, just put it on my bill."

How do you make an elephant float?

Two scoops of ice cream, some root beer, and an elephant.

Why did the toilet paper roll down the hill?

It wanted to get to the bottom.

What goes ouch, ouch, ouch, ouch, ouch, ouch, ouch, ouch, ouch?

An octopus with tight shoes.

Termite goes into a bar and asks, "Is the bar tender here?"

Who was the idiot who put the letter "s" in "lisp"?

You: How can you keep a fool in suspense?

Your friend: How?

You:

How do you keep a skunk from smelling?

Hold its nose.

What do you call a clairvoyant short person who just broke out of prison?

A small medium at large.

Why did the bunnies go on strike?

They wanted a raise in celery.

The Case Against Chores

A lot of kids know they don't want to do chores, but they may need help coming up with a reason not to do them. To solve that problem, here are a few handy arguments:

"Let's not clean. Let's move!"

"Mom, seriously. Our time together is so short. Let's not waste it 'cleaning'."

"'Cleanliness' is NOT next to 'Godliness.' It's next to 'clay.' I looked it up."

"My room isn't a mess, it's a personal expression. It took me a long time to make it like this. If I were to change it in any way *(lower voice)*, I would be untrue to myself, AND *(sniff, sniff)* my art."

"My room is not messy, it's a science project. 'Entropy' — look it up."

"This is my unique filing system. If we 'clean' it, I'll never find anything."

"Why do the dishes? You know they're only going to get dirty again."

*On your former
friend's arm*

How to Draw
a Mouse

Ask a friend to trust you for a moment. You're going to show them how to draw a cute little mouse on their hand.

Here's how it goes:

"First, you draw a little tiny nose."

"Then, a pair of cute little eyes..."

1 Draw a little dot.

2 Draw two more little dots.

3 Draw a big line up
the arm. And run.

Physics
gets phun!

The Home Tennis Ball Launcher!

You'll need a basketball and a tennis ball. Stack them as shown.

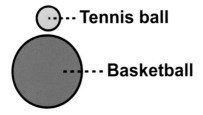

Tennis ball

Basketball

Then drop the stack onto the ground, making sure you're out of the way. The tennis ball will shoot straight up and the basketball will stop dead.

Try this:
For even more impressive results, try the same thing with a Ping-Pong® ball instead of a tennis ball.

How to Play the Telephone

Next time you're on the phone to a friend and they question your musical talent, play them a tune! Hit the buttons as shown. Your friend will hear the tune.

London Bridge

9 #   9 6 3 6   9
Lon-don Bridge is fall-ing down,

2 3 6   3 6   9
fall-ing down, fall-ing down.

9 #   9 6 3 6   9
Lon-don Bridge is fall-ing down,

2 9 3 1
my fair la-dy.

America

5   5   6   1   5 9
My coun-try, 'tis of thee,

0   0   8 0 8 4
sweet land of li-ber-ty,

8   4 2 4
of thee I sing.

Twinkle, Twinkle, Little Star

1   1   9   9 0 0 9
Twin-kle, twin-kle, lit-tle star

Happy Birthday

4   4   2   4 # 8   1   1   2   1 9 8
Hap-py birth-day to you, hap-py birth-day to you

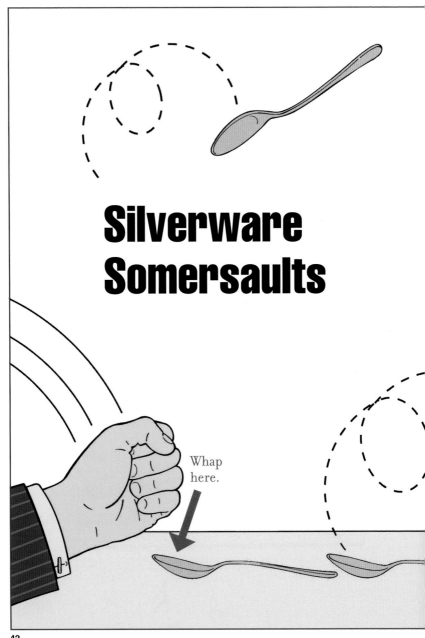

Silverware Somersaults

Whap here.

You are sitting at a restaurant table with other people. You are eating, or waiting for your food, or maybe everyone is just staring blankly at everyone else. In any event, you are NOT being amazing. How do you fix this picture?

1 Arrange two spoons and a glass as shown. Make sure the spoons overlap.

2 Then make everyone hush, take a deep breath, and suddenly whap where it says to. Do it right — not too hard and not too soft — and the spoon (or fork) will execute a beautiful single flip and drop into the glass. Three points.

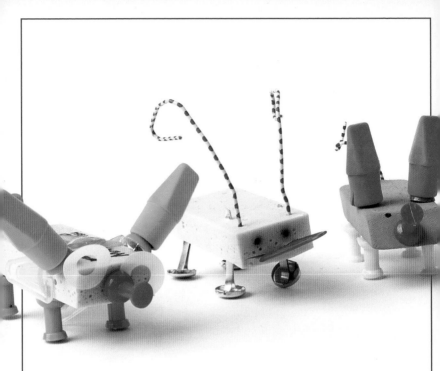

School Supplies

Gone **CRAZY**

Have you ever wondered what all that stuff in your pencil case is for?

Build a Bridge for Pennies

Welcome to the fast-growing world of penny stacking. We provide here a set of instructions for your basic 43-cent bridge, but there is much more out there (see the internet, as usual). No glue, no tape, no cheats. All you need are steady hands and a pocketful of pennies.

1 Build a tower like this one.

2 On top of THAT tower add three more pennies.

3 Then build a matching tower and connect the two as shown.

Snorting Rubber Bands

Another bit of no-practice magic, located in the Eeeeuuuw category. You'll need a rubber band and a nose.

Oink!

1 Hook rubber band over pinkie. Stretch it and hold by your nose. Smile.

2 Make a huge snorting noise. Let the band snap back into your hand.

3

Cough and
let the band
hang out.

Clonk Your Head on a Wall

Kick wall.

Walk toward a lamppost or wall. Then, just before you bump into it, kick it loudly and "bounce" back, holding your forehead and moaning.

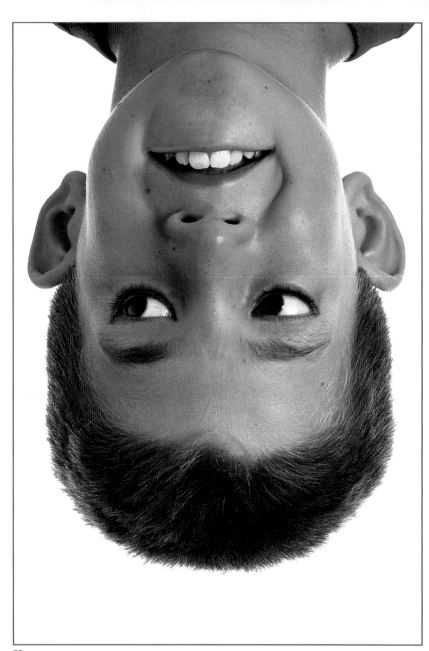

Anything Wrong with Brad?

This is one of our favorite optical illusions. If you can't figure out what's wrong by staring at the picture, just flip it over. The answer will become very clear, trust us.

Be a Rubber Band Ninja Warrior

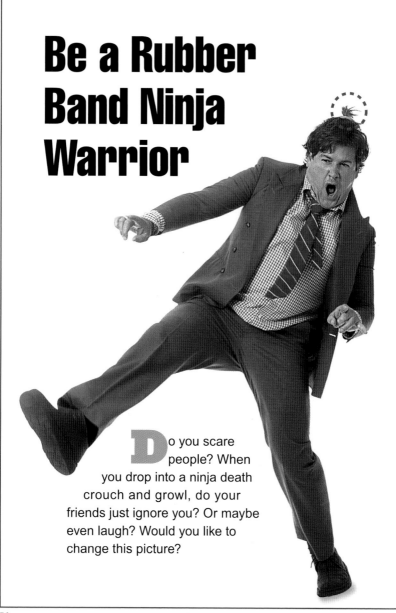

Do you scare people? When you drop into a ninja death crouch and growl, do your friends just ignore you? Or maybe even laugh? Would you like to change this picture?

Find a fat
rubber band.

Place on head, at
hairline (above
forehead).

It should start
to crawl up your
head on its own.

Ninja!

Here's How

Place a fat rubber band around your
head as shown. Carefully push it up
until you start to feel it move on its
own toward the top of your head.
Immediately drop into your ninja
crouch, growl, and shift around until
the rubber band makes its final slide
up. Unless you're bald, at the very top
of your head it should grab a samurai
topknot of hair. At that instant, make
a horrible face and freeze into your
most menacing pose.

Works.

Doesn't.

Some rubber
bands work,
some don't. A
little flour on the
band makes it
slipperier, too.

We Control Your Foot

You may think you are the one in charge of your foot, but you would be wrong if you did. Because we are. And here's the proof.

Sit down. Lift your right foot off the ground. Swing it around in a clockwise circle.

With your foot still circling, draw the number 6 in the air with your right hand.

When you do that, we will cause your foot to stop and reverse direction. Try to defy us as many times as you want. You are powerless.

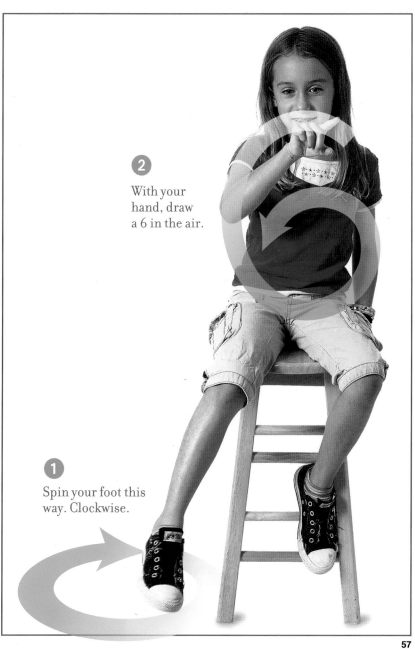

2

With your hand, draw a 6 in the air.

1

Spin your foot this way. Clockwise.

Carve a
BARFKIN

Have you ever wondered what to do with all the stuff that was inside your pumpkin? Answer: Just leave it there!

Ping-Pong®
Ball Burbling

Although there are many ways to play with a Ping-Pong ball, not many of them are as breathtaking as this one. You'll need one Ping-Pong ball and some lung power. If you've ever seen a beach ball hovering on a jet of air at a store, then you have seen the same scientific principle at work. Replace the beach ball with a Ping-Pong ball, and the air blower with you.

Place the ball carefully on your beautifully pursed lips. Then very, very, very slowly… begin blowing. If you filled your lungs with air, like we should have told you at the start, you might be able to get it to levitate like we did (on our fourth try).

For cheaters. Use a funnel. Blow through the narrow end.

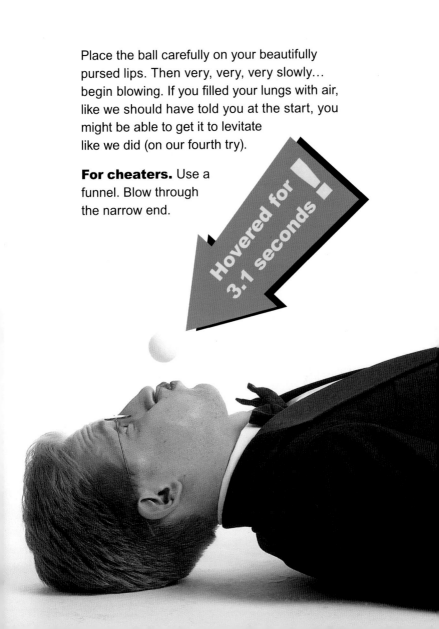

Hovered for 3.1 seconds

How to Stick a Pencil in Your Ear

Backstage View

Slide pencil through hand.

...and take it back out of your nose

After you learn this one, you'll wonder how you ever got along without it. It's that useful.

We used a pencil in these photographs, but don't let that limit you. You can stick all sorts of things in your ear. If you're in the kitchen, try a carrot; if you're in a restaurant, try a fork or spoon.

The hand moves... not the pencil.

Backstage View

Slide hand down pencil.

Note: Eraser is touching jacket.

Quarter Snatching

This is one of those tricks everyone's favorite uncle does — or at least he should. Load up your arm with quarters — one if you're a rank beginner, four if you've got mad skills. Then swoop your hand down and catch them all mid-air. Speed and confidence — that's all it takes.

1 Load

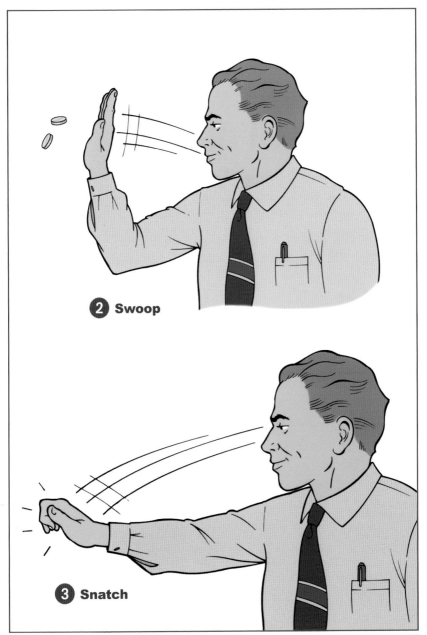

2 Swoop

3 Snatch

The Broom and Water Scam

The next time you're in the kitchen and someone there needs something to do, try this.

1 Fill a plastic or paper cup with water.

2 Get up on the counter and press the cup to the ceiling.

3 Ask your victim to get a broom and hold the cup to the ceiling while you get down.

That's it. You're done. Now you can wander off. What are they going to do? (Except maybe wonder why it is they ever do anything you ask them to.)

Lame magic
The Floating Fork

Are you completely unreasonable? Do you want to be an incredible magician? But without spending any time on the boring practice part?

So do we!

Here's one trick that will help. You need to be at dinner with some friends.

1. Stick a knife into the tines of a fork and cover both with a napkin. Don't let anyone see you do this part.

2. Lift the napkin (and fork) as shown. Close your eyes and say a lot of things like *"boooga woooga wooo"* as you lift the fork (with your thumb) into and out of view.

WOW!

3.

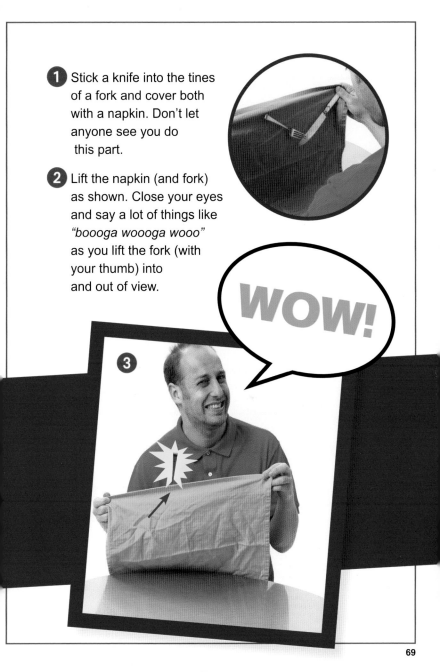

You Could Put Your Eye Out with That

This is based on the famous "fork in the eye" trick, a piece of genius created by the amazing magician Mac King. Try it when you're at a restaurant with friends.

1 When no one is paying attention, pick up one of those plastic containers filled with liquid creamer. Pry the lid open a little or poke a hole in it. Hide the container in your hand and make a fist. Don't let it leak. Yet.

> Feels like something's in my eye...

> ...something really sharp...

2 Complain about something in your eye. Keep complaining until people finally start paying attention. When they do…

3 Bring your fist to your eye and start rubbing. Say "Owww. Feels like something really SHARP in my eye!"

4 Rub harder and harder and finally squeeze and...

5

Eeeeeek!

How to Mess Up Family Portraits

THE SELF-STRANGLE

THE HIGH
WAIST

THE
BARF

Drop me a shoe
Flip-Flop Mail

Flip-flops make lovely postcards — no packaging necessary! Write your message on the bottom and put the stamps and address on the top. You have to add extra postage to cover the hand canceling, but we've gotten flip-flop messages through the mail and been deeply moved.

To: John Cassidy
Klutz
450 Lambert Av.
Palo Alto, CA 94306

You could probably do the same with tennis shoes, although you'd have to remove the laces and stinky insoles first. Plus, you'd have to staple the stamps since tape is a no-no over stamps. Try it.

This shoe went through the mail no problem. New York to Palo Alto.

KLUTZ/CASS
450 LAMBERT
PALO ALTO, CA 94306

Message on bottom.

The classic

Putting on a Kick Me Sticker

1 Inspire trust. Offer chair.

2 Place sticker.

BIO-
HAZARD
LEVEL 4

HOW DO YOU
LIKE MY
WALKING
?
1-800-DONTCARE

FREE
PIGGY-
BACKS!
HOP
ON!

EXPLOSIVES
STAY
BACK!

MAKES
WIDE
TURNS

BLASTING
ZONE

Orange Peel Dentures

If you're tired of paying big bucks to get your teeth whitened, or if you'd like your teeth to make more of a statement about who you are, this could be your item.

Cut an orange in half.

In half again.

Peel.

Trim off the points.

Like so.

Cut teeth.

Done.

(P.S. Our photographer, a seasoned professional, had to be led from the studio until he could recover himself enough to take this picture. It's that funny.)

Wear with pride.

How to Catch Popcorn on Your Tongue

We used to think that catching food in your mouth was just one of those skills — like being able to curl your tongue — that you either had or didn't. It took Jeff Raz, who teaches clowning in San Francisco, to demonstrate how wrong we were. You can actually achieve greatness at catching food in your mouth if you simply follow Jeff's food-catching rules:

1. Stick your tongue out and catch on your tongue. Not in your mouth.

2. Lock onto your target as it hits the peak of its arc. Don't try to follow it with your eyes all the way in. (Doesn't work and actually creates more problems.)

Your House, the Jungle Gym

Have you ever wondered what you'd do if your hallway were covered in hot lava? Don't you think a little practice and planning now, when it's safe, makes a lot more sense than later, after some volcano goes off and there's no time to "figure it out?"

What follows are simple steps for climbing down a hallway without touching the floor. By the way, if anyone comes by and asks, you're conducting a "hot lava in the hallway safety drill."

HALLWAY CLIMBING TWO WAYS

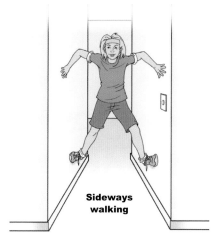

Sideways walking

Scouching sideways

DOORNASTICS

Doorway chin-ups

Doorway climbing

Write a *"first-time sentence"*

Your Brain Smells Like Moon Pie Dumplings

The Challenge: Construct a sentence that makes some kind of sense, but that NO ONE, in the history of history, has ever ever said or written before. When you think you've done it, fill in the blank below.

Extra credit Use a marker and write your sentence on the bottom of a flip-flop. Then mail to us with no package. See page 2 for our address and page 74 for mailing instructions. If you do, we will send you our *You Are an Amazing Person* certificate.

Fill in the blanks

The sentence below has never been written or said before in the English language. You read it here first.

_____

_____

_____

_____

_____

Paper Cup Honk Machine

To make a noisemaker guaranteed to annoy anyone in earshot, all you need is a paper cup, twine or thick string, a sharp pencil, and a damp paper towel.

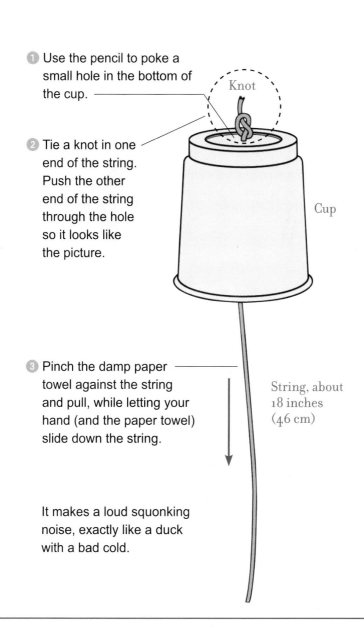

1. Use the pencil to poke a small hole in the bottom of the cup.

Knot

2. Tie a knot in one end of the string. Push the other end of the string through the hole so it looks like the picture.

Cup

3. Pinch the damp paper towel against the string and pull, while letting your hand (and the paper towel) slide down the string.

String, about 18 inches (46 cm)

It makes a loud squonking noise, exactly like a duck with a bad cold.

Eat Dead Flies... and Like Them

Roll a magazine up (or use a flyswatter) and chase a fly around the room. When it lands, smash it. Then, make sure someone with a weak stomach is watching and pull the dead fly off the magazine and pop it in your mouth. Yum! **P.S.** If you want to cheat — like we did — put a raisin on the magazine before the whole scam starts.

SPLAT!

YUM!

Snap Tops

It's amazing, sometimes, how small skills can lead to big social results.

Learn this little item and you will dominate the social food chain at your home, school, or workplace.

Almost any kind of plastic lid works.

15–20 feet (3–6 m), no problem

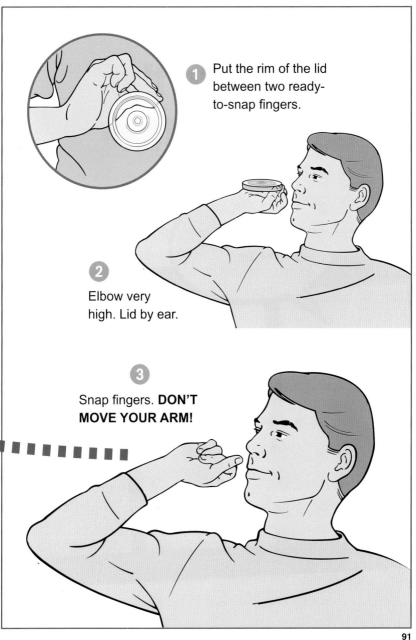

1. Put the rim of the lid between two ready-to-snap fingers.

2. Elbow very high. Lid by ear.

3. Snap fingers. **DON'T MOVE YOUR ARM!**

How to Do the Deadly Selfnap

92

A friend of ours gave us this little bit. Her father, she says, would always use it as his exit after telling them their goodnight story when she was little.

"Traumatized me for years," she said.

Tin Can Telephone

There's a category of toys and skills that everyone (especially parents) remembers fondly from ye olde tymes when life was simpler and far better. Things like secret ink you can make from lemon juice, or kites you can make from newspaper, or bottle rockets, or dandelion tea, etc., etc.

Here's the standard line: "Why do you need video games? Granddad used to play with all these simple toys, back before TV and all that."

Well, all we can say is, if he did, he must have been a very frustrated guy, probably with a finger or two missing. Because lemon juice ink that shows up on a letter when you heat it just doesn't work. Nor does a newspaper kite. A bottle rocket using black powder is both illegal and incredibly dangerous (although exciting, we'll confess), and dandelion tea tastes exactly like hot, bitter water.

Punch a hole in the bottom of the can and knot the string through it.

But we will admit one thing: Tin can telephones actually do work. We were dubious, too, but we made a pair, and they work even if you just whisper. Keep the line tight. Who knew?

Are you ready for mime time?

How to Lean on Things That Aren't There

THE SECRET?
A lot of weight
is on this foot.

Teh Cas Aginst Gud Spelg

Aoccdrnig to rscheearch at Cmabrigde Uinervtisy, it deosn't mttaer in waht oredr the ltteers in a wrod are. The olny iprmoatnt tihng is taht the frist and lsat ltteer be in the rghit plcae. The rset can be a taotl mses and you can sitll raed it wouthit a porbelm. Tihs is bcuseae the huamn mnid deos not raed ervey lteter by istlef, but the wrod as a wlohe. Amzanig, huh?

Shiw Tihs Two Yur Tchr!!!

Acknowledgments

**The Genius Behind All
That Is Immature**.................John Cassidy

Editor ....Pat Murphy

Design...................................Kevin Plottner

Illustration ....Buc Rogers

Photography ....Peter Fox, Liz Hutnick,
Katrine Naleid, Paula Weed

Creative Director.................Michael Sherman

Art Direction........................Kate Paddock, Jill Turney

Production...........................Kelly Shaffer, Linda Olbourne

Help......................................Julie Collings, Theresa Hutnick,
Dan Roddick, Michael Stroud

Production Editor ....Madeleine Robins

Editorial Assistance ....Valerie Wyatt, Dan Letchworth

Permissions ....MaryBeth Arago

More Help

David Barker, Laurie Bryan, Nathan Diehl, Paul Doherty, Susan Fox,
Vicki Friedberg, Sheri Haab, Bill Harley, Georgia Herzog, Jenny Hsin,
Barb Magnus, Gary Mcdonald, Daniel Miller, Karen Phillips, Don Rathjen

Models

Bill Olson, The Chu Family, Daniel Miller, Hamish Forsythe, Hannah
Tuminaro, James Harrison, Jenner Fox, Jim Baer, John Cassidy, Josh
Schneck, Kael Price, Kaela Fox, Lauren Kucik, The Lawson Family, Martini
Chorba, Nathan Diehl, Sean Chapman, Sergio Valente, Travis Bowers,
Tup Fisher, The Zenger Family

Credits

Page 1: frame, iStockphoto/Thinkstock; Page 9: orange, iStockphoto.com/
Ljupco; Page 10: Harold and Esther Edgerton Foundation, 2007, courtesy
of Palm Press, Inc.; Page 38: tennis ball, iStockphoto/Thinkstock; Page 46:
pennies, iStockphoto.com/bpalmer; Page 72: frames, istockphoto.com/
sub; iStockphoto.com/LostSax; iStockphoto.com/gbrundin;
Page 86: duck, iStockphoto.com/resonants

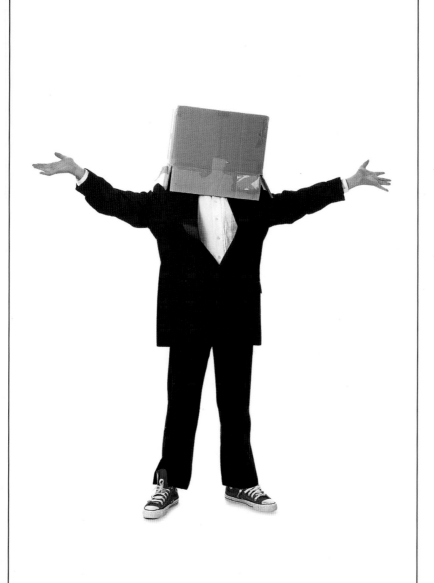

MAIL-IN REBATE

NOT PAYABLE AT RETAIL

TO RECEIVE YOUR MAIL-IN REBATE CHECK YOU MUST:

❶ Purchase ONE (1) new copy of the full version of *The Encyclopedia of Immaturity, The Encyclopedia of Immaturity Volume 2,* and/or *The Klutz Book of Inventions.* (This offer does not apply to the Scholastic Book Clubs editions of these books, to *The Encyclopedia of Immaturity — Short Attention Span Edition*, or to *The Klutz Book of Inventions — Hall of Fame Edition*.) You will receive a rebate of $3 for each qualifying title you buy.

❷ Mail your original register receipt for the above book(s) along with this completed rebate form (not a copy) to:

"The World According to Klutz Offer"
c/o Klutz, 450 Lambert Avenue
Palo Alto, CA 94306

NOTE: REBATE OFFER VALID ONLY ON PURCHASES MADE AFTER JULY 1, 2013,
AND ALL REBATE REQUESTS MUST BE POSTMARKED BY
DECEMBER 31, 2015 AND RECEIVED BY JANUARY 31, 2016.

Rebate check should be made payable to:

Name: _____

Address: _____

City: _____

State/Province/Territory: _____ Zip Code/Postal Code: _____

Email (optional): _____ U.S. Canada (circle one)

To receive the full $9 in rebates, you must buy one copy of each title.
What did you buy?

❏ *The Encyclopedia of Immaturity*

❏ *The Encyclopedia of Immaturity Volume 2*

❏ *The Klutz Book of Inventions*